PAPER PEONY PRESS

This journal belongs to:

_____

place
photo
here

photo details:_____

_____

_____

How we found out we were pregnant...

_____
_____
_____
_____
_____
_____
_____
_____
_____
_____
_____
_____
_____
_____
_____
_____

and how we're feeling about it...

_____
_____
_____
_____
_____
_____
_____

THE DUE DATE:

FIRST SONOGRAM

place
photo
here

DATE:	GESTATIONAL AGE:
LOCATION:	
NOTES:	

MILESTONES

first time you...   *week #*

○ took a positive pregnancy test

○ had a prenatal appointment

○ experienced morning sickness

○ food aversion

○ heard baby's heartbeat

○ had a sonogram

○ shared the news

○ had a strong food craving

○ wore maternity clothes

○ found out gender

○ bought a baby item

○ had a baby shower

○ felt baby kick

○ had someone ask if you were pregnant

○ felt baby hiccups

○ received unsolicited advice

○ ate a snack at 3am

○ prepared baby's room

○ felt a contraction

○ held your baby!

BOY NAMES

name:

suggested by:

GIRL NAMES

name:

suggested by:

APPOINTMENTS

date	weeks	weight	blood pressure	fundal height	baby's heart rate
/ /					
/ /					
/ /					
/ /					
/ /					
/ /					
/ /					
/ /					
/ /					
/ /					
/ /					
/ /					
/ /					
/ /					

ADDITIONAL NOTES:

APPOINTMENTS

BABY SHOWERS

DATE: _____

LOCATION: _____

HOSTED BY: _____

GIFT:	FROM:	TY

BABY SHOWERS

DATE: _____

LOCATION: _____

HOSTED BY: _____

GIFT:	FROM:	TY

TODAY'S DATE: _____

PRENATAL APPOINTMENT: ⌐YES⌐ / ⌐NO⌐

HIGHLIGHTS

ENERGY

1   5
O——O——O——O——O

MOOD

O——O——O——O——O

SLEEP

O——O——O——O——O

BABY SIZE:
poppy seed

CRAVINGS:

- _____
- _____
- _____
- _____

AVERSIONS:

- _____
- _____
- _____
- _____

36 WEEKS *to go*

THINGS I WANT TO REMEMBER:

· trimester 1 ·

TODAY'S DATE: _____

PRENATAL APPOINTMENT:　　⊏ YES ⊐　　/　　⊏ NO ⊐

HIGHLIGHTS

ENERGY

1　○――○――○――○――○　5

MOOD

○――○――○――○――○

SLEEP

○――○――○――○――○

BABY SIZE:
apple seed

CRAVINGS:

- _____
- _____
- _____
- _____

AVERSIONS:

- _____
- _____
- _____
- _____

35 WEEKS *to go*

THINGS I WANT TO REMEMBER:

TODAY'S DATE: _____

PRENATAL APPOINTMENT: ⊏ YES ⊐   /   ⊏ NO ⊐

HIGHLIGHTS

ENERGY

1 ○————○————○————○————○ 5

MOOD

○————○————○————○————○

SLEEP

○————○————○————○————○

BABY SIZE:
sweet pea

CRAVINGS:

-
-
-
-

AVERSIONS:

-
-
-
-

34 WEEKS *to go*

THINGS I WANT TO REMEMBER:

· **trimester 1** ·

TODAY'S DATE: _____

PRENATAL APPOINTMENT: ⌐ YES ⌐   /   ⌐ NO ⌐

HIGHLIGHTS

ENERGY

1   5
○———○———○———○———○

MOOD

○———○———○———○———○

SLEEP

○———○———○———○———○

BABY SIZE: *blueberry*	

CRAVINGS:

• _____

• _____

• _____

• _____

AVERSIONS:

• _____

• _____

• _____

• _____

33 **WEEKS** *to go*

THINGS I WANT TO REMEMBER:

TODAY'S DATE: _____

PRENATAL APPOINTMENT: ⊏ YES ⊐   /   ⊏ NO ⊐

┌─────────── HIGHLIGHTS ───────────┐

ENERGY

1 ──O────O────O────O────O── 5

MOOD

O────O────O────O────O

SLEEP

O────O────O────O────O

| BABY SIZE: *raspberry* | |

CRAVINGS:

- _____
- _____
- _____
- _____

AVERSIONS:

- _____
- _____
- _____
- _____

32 WEEKS *to go*

┌─────── THINGS I WANT TO REMEMBER: ───────┐

TODAY'S DATE: _____

PRENATAL APPOINTMENT: ⊏ YES ⊐ / ⊏ NO ⊐

┌─────── HIGHLIGHTS ───────┐

ENERGY

1   5
○────○────○────○────○

MOOD

○────○────○────○────○

SLEEP

○────○────○────○────○

| BABY SIZE: *grape* | |

CRAVINGS:

- _____
- _____
- _____
- _____

AVERSIONS:

- _____
- _____
- _____
- _____

31 WEEKS *to go*

┌─────── THINGS I WANT TO REMEMBER: ───────┐

└──┘

OH BABY

BABY PREP CHECKLIST

TODAY'S DATE: _____

PRENATAL APPOINTMENT: ⊏ YES ⊐ / ⊏ NO ⊐

―――― HIGHLIGHTS ――――

ENERGY

1   5
○―――○―――○―――○―――○

MOOD

○―――○―――○―――○―――○

SLEEP

○―――○―――○―――○―――○

BABY SIZE: *prune*	

CRAVINGS:

- _____
- _____
- _____
- _____

AVERSIONS:

- _____
- _____
- _____
- _____

30 WEEKS *to go*

―――― THINGS I WANT TO REMEMBER: ――――

TODAY'S DATE: _____

PRENATAL APPOINTMENT: ⊏ YES ⊐ / ⊏ NO ⊐

―――― HIGHLIGHTS ――――

ENERGY

1   5

O――O――O――O――O

MOOD

O――O――O――O――O

SLEEP

O――O――O――O――O

BABY SIZE: *lime*	

CRAVINGS:

- _____
- _____
- _____
- _____

AVERSIONS:

- _____
- _____
- _____
- _____

⬤⬤⬤⬤⬤⬤⬤⬤⬤⬤◯◯◯◯◯◯◯◯
⬤⬤⬤⬤⬤⬤⬤⬤⬤⬤⬤◯◯◯◯◯◯◯ **29** **WEEKS** *to go*

―――― THINGS I WANT TO REMEMBER: ――――

TODAY'S DATE: _____

PRENATAL APPOINTMENT: ⊏ YES ⊐ / ⊏ NO ⊐

HIGHLIGHTS

ENERGY

1   5
○———○———○———○———○

MOOD

○———○———○———○———○

SLEEP

○———○———○———○———○

BABY SIZE: *plum*	

CRAVINGS:

· _____
· _____
· _____
· _____

AVERSIONS:

· _____
· _____
· _____
· _____

28 WEEKS *to go*

THINGS I WANT TO REMEMBER:

TODAY'S DATE: _____

PRENATAL APPOINTMENT: ⊏ YES ⊐ / ⊏ NO ⊐

┌─── HIGHLIGHTS ───┐

ENERGY

1   5
○──────○──────○──────○──────○

MOOD

○──────○──────○──────○──────○

SLEEP

○──────○──────○──────○──────○

| BABY SIZE: *peach* | |

CRAVINGS:

- _____
- _____
- _____
- _____

AVERSIONS:

- _____
- _____
- _____
- _____

27 **WEEKS** *to go*

┌─── THINGS I WANT TO REMEMBER: ───┐

First trimester reflections....

place
photo
here

photo details:

GENDER PREDICTIONS

team
BOY

○ _____

○ _____

○ _____

○ _____

○ _____

○ _____

○ _____

○ _____

○ _____

○ _____

○ _____

○ _____

○ _____

○ _____

○ _____

team
GIRL

○ _____

○ _____

○ _____

○ _____

○ _____

○ _____

○ _____

○ _____

○ _____

○ _____

○ _____

○ _____

○ _____

○ _____

○ _____

TODAY'S DATE: _____

PRENATAL APPOINTMENT: ⊏ YES ⊐ / ⊏ NO ⊐

┌─── **HIGHLIGHTS** ───┐

ENERGY

1   5
○——○——○——○——○

MOOD

○——○——○——○——○

SLEEP

○——○——○——○——○

BABY SIZE:
lemon

CRAVINGS:

- _____
- _____
- _____
- _____

AVERSIONS:

- _____
- _____
- _____
- _____

26 **WEEKS** *to go*

┌─── **THINGS I WANT TO REMEMBER:** ───┐

TODAY'S DATE: _____

PRENATAL APPOINTMENT: ⌐YES⌐   /   ⌐NO⌐

HIGHLIGHTS

ENERGY

1 ———————————————— 5
O——O——O——O——O

MOOD

O——O——O——O——O

SLEEP

O——O——O——O——O

| BABY SIZE: *apple* | |

CRAVINGS:

• _____

• _____

• _____

• _____

AVERSIONS:

• _____

• _____

• _____

• _____

25 WEEKS *to go*

THINGS I WANT TO REMEMBER:

TODAY'S DATE: _____

PRENATAL APPOINTMENT: ⊏ YES ⊐ / ⊏ NO ⊐

HIGHLIGHTS

ENERGY

1 ○——○——○——○——○ 5

MOOD

○——○——○——○——○

SLEEP

○——○——○——○——○

BABY SIZE: *avocado*

CRAVINGS:

- _____
- _____
- _____
- _____

AVERSIONS:

- _____
- _____
- _____
- _____

24 WEEKS *to go*

THINGS I WANT TO REMEMBER:

· trimester 2 ·

TODAY'S DATE: _____

PRENATAL APPOINTMENT: ⊏ YES ⊐ / ⊏ NO ⊐

HIGHLIGHTS

ENERGY

1   5
○————○————○————○————○

MOOD

○————○————○————○————○

SLEEP

○————○————○————○————○

| BABY SIZE: *turnip* | |

CRAVINGS:

- _____
- _____
- _____
- _____

AVERSIONS:

- _____
- _____
- _____
- _____

●●●●●●●●●●●●●●●●●○○○
●●●●●●●●●●●●●●●●●●○○ **23** **WEEKS** *to go*

THINGS I WANT TO REMEMBER:

TODAY'S DATE: _____

PRENATAL APPOINTMENT:　　☐ YES ☐　　/　　☐ NO ☐

┌─────── HIGHLIGHTS ───────┐

ENERGY

1　　　　　　　　　　　　　　5
○────○────○────○────○

MOOD

○────○────○────○────○

SLEEP

○────○────○────○────○

BABY SIZE:
sweet potato

CRAVINGS:

- _____
- _____
- _____
- _____

AVERSIONS:

- _____
- _____
- _____
- _____

22 WEEKS *to go*

┌─────── THINGS I WANT TO REMEMBER: ───────┐

TODAY'S DATE: _____

PRENATAL APPOINTMENT: ⊏ YES ⊐ / ⊏ NO ⊐

HIGHLIGHTS

ENERGY

1 ○——○——○——○——○ 5

MOOD

○——○——○——○——○

SLEEP

○——○——○——○——○

BABY SIZE: *tomato*	

CRAVINGS:

- _____
- _____
- _____
- _____

AVERSIONS:

- _____
- _____
- _____
- _____

21 WEEKS *to go*

THINGS I WANT TO REMEMBER:

TODAY'S DATE: _____

PRENATAL APPOINTMENT: ⊏ YES ⊐ / ⊏ NO ⊐

HIGHLIGHTS

ENERGY

1   5
○———○———○———○———○

MOOD

○———○———○———○———○

SLEEP

○———○———○———○———○

| BABY SIZE: *banana* | |

CRAVINGS:

- _____
- _____
- _____
- _____

AVERSIONS:

- _____
- _____
- _____
- _____

20 WEEKS *to go*

THINGS I WANT TO REMEMBER:

½

Halfway there!

THIS LIFE IS SURE TO BE A WONDERFUL ADVENTURE.

TODAY'S DATE: _____

PRENATAL APPOINTMENT: ⊏YES⊐   /   ⊏NO⊐

HIGHLIGHTS

ENERGY

1 ○———○———○———○———○ 5

MOOD

○———○———○———○———○

SLEEP

○———○———○———○———○

BABY SIZE: *carrot*	

CRAVINGS:

- _____
- _____
- _____
- _____

AVERSIONS:

- _____
- _____
- _____
- _____

19 **WEEKS** *to go*

THINGS I WANT TO REMEMBER:

TODAY'S DATE: _____

PRENATAL APPOINTMENT: ⊏YES⊐ / ⊏NO⊐

┌─── **HIGHLIGHTS** ───┐

ENERGY

1   5
○——○——○——○——○

MOOD

○——○——○——○——○

SLEEP

○——○——○——○——○

| BABY SIZE: *papaya* | |

CRAVINGS:

- _____
- _____
- _____
- _____

AVERSIONS:

- _____
- _____
- _____
- _____

18 **WEEKS** *to go*

┌─── **THINGS I WANT TO REMEMBER:** ───┐

TODAY'S DATE: _____

PRENATAL APPOINTMENT: ⊏ YES ⊐ / ⊏ NO ⊐

HIGHLIGHTS

ENERGY
1 ─○─○─○─○─○ 5

MOOD
○─○─○─○─○

SLEEP
○─○─○─○─○

BABY SIZE: *grapefruit*

CRAVINGS:
- _____
- _____
- _____
- _____

AVERSIONS:
- _____
- _____
- _____
- _____

17 WEEKS *to go*

THINGS I WANT TO REMEMBER:

TODAY'S DATE: _____

PRENATAL APPOINTMENT: ⊏ YES ⊐   /   ⊏ NO ⊐

HIGHLIGHTS

ENERGY
1 ○———○———○———○———○ 5

MOOD
○———○———○———○———○

SLEEP
○———○———○———○———○

BABY SIZE:
ear of corn

CRAVINGS:

* _____
* _____
* _____
* _____

AVERSIONS:

* _____
* _____
* _____
* _____

16 WEEKS *to go*

THINGS I WANT TO REMEMBER:

TODAY'S DATE: _____

PRENATAL APPOINTMENT: ⊏ YES ⊐   /   ⊏ NO ⊐

HIGHLIGHTS

ENERGY

1   5
○———○———○———○———○

MOOD

○———○———○———○———○

SLEEP

○———○———○———○———○

BABY SIZE:
rutabaga

CRAVINGS:

-
-
-
-

AVERSIONS:

-
-
-
-

15 WEEKS *to go*

THINGS I WANT TO REMEMBER:

TODAY'S DATE: _____

PRENATAL APPOINTMENT: ⊏ YES ⊐   /   ⊏ NO ⊐

HIGHLIGHTS

ENERGY

1   5
○——○——○——○——○

MOOD

○——○——○——○——○

SLEEP

○——○——○——○——○

| BABY SIZE: *lettuce* | |

CRAVINGS:

- _____
- _____
- _____
- _____

AVERSIONS:

- _____
- _____
- _____
- _____

14 WEEKS *to go*

THINGS I WANT TO REMEMBER:

Second trimester reflections....

place
photo
here

photo details:_____

_____

_____

Coming down the home stretch...

Hospital bag checklist:

 ## MOM

- ○ pillow
- ○ socks
- ○ nursing bra / sports bra
- ○ PJs
- ○ robe
- ○ underwear
- ○ maxi pads
- ○ nursing pads
- ○ going home clothes

 ## BABY

- ○ diapers
- ○ wipes
- ○ pacifiers
- ○ receiving blanket
- ○ scratch mittens
- ○ hat
- ○ nursing pillow
- ○ going home outfit
- ○ car seat

 ## TOILETRIES

- ○ toothbrush / toothpaste
- ○ deodorant
- ○ shampoo
- ○ brush
- ○ glasses / contacts
- ○ chapstick
- ○ hair tie
- ○ nipple cream

 ## DAD

- ○ pillow
- ○ toothbrush / toothpaste
- ○ deodorant
- ○ camera
- ○ ID. & insurance
- ○ cell phone / charger
- ○ pen
- ○ birth plan

 ## EXTRAS

- ○ cards
- ○ white noise machine
- ○ snacks
- ○ magazines / book

 ## OTHER

- ○ _____
- ○ _____
- ○ _____
- ○ _____
- ○ _____
- ○ _____
- ○ _____
- ○ _____
- ○ _____
- ○ _____
- ○ _____
- ○ _____
- ○ _____

TODAY'S DATE: _____

PRENATAL APPOINTMENT: ⌐YES⌐   /   ⌐NO⌐

---HIGHLIGHTS---

ENERGY

1   5
O—O—O—O—O

MOOD

O—O—O—O—O

SLEEP

O—O—O—O—O

BABY SIZE: *cauliflower*	

CRAVINGS:

- _____
- _____
- _____
- _____

AVERSIONS:

- _____
- _____
- _____
- _____

13 **WEEKS** *to go*

---THINGS I WANT TO REMEMBER:---

TODAY'S DATE: _____

PRENATAL APPOINTMENT: ⊏ YES ⊐   /   ⊏ NO ⊐

HIGHLIGHTS

ENERGY

1   5
○——○——○——○——○

MOOD

○——○——○——○——○

SLEEP

○——○——○——○——○

BABY SIZE:
eggplant

CRAVINGS:

- _____
- _____
- _____
- _____

AVERSIONS:

- _____
- _____
- _____
- _____

12 WEEKS *to go*

THINGS I WANT TO REMEMBER:

TODAY'S DATE: _____

PRENATAL APPOINTMENT: ⊏ YES ⊐   /   ⊏ NO ⊐

┌─── HIGHLIGHTS ───┐

ENERGY

1   5
○────○────○────○────○

MOOD

○────○────○────○────○

SLEEP

○────○────○────○────○

BABY SIZE: *acorn squash*	

CRAVINGS:

- _____
- _____
- _____
- _____

AVERSIONS:

- _____
- _____
- _____
- _____

11 **WEEKS** *to go*

┌─── THINGS I WANT TO REMEMBER: ───┐

TODAY'S DATE: _____

PRENATAL APPOINTMENT: ⊏YES⊐   /   ⊏NO⊐

HIGHLIGHTS

ENERGY

1   5
○——○——○——○——○

MOOD

○——○——○——○——○

SLEEP

○——○——○——○——○

BABY SIZE: *cabbage*

CRAVINGS:

● _____
● _____
● _____
● _____

AVERSIONS:

● _____
● _____
● _____
● _____

10 WEEKS *to go*

THINGS I WANT TO REMEMBER:

TODAY'S DATE: _____

PRENATAL APPOINTMENT: ⊏ YES ⊐   /   ⊏ NO ⊐

HIGHLIGHTS

ENERGY

1 ○————○————○————○————○ 5

MOOD

○————○————○————○————○

SLEEP

○————○————○————○————○

BABY SIZE: *coconut*	

CRAVINGS:

- _____
- _____
- _____
- _____

AVERSIONS:

- _____
- _____
- _____
- _____

9 WEEKS *to go*

THINGS I WANT TO REMEMBER:

TODAY'S DATE: _____

PRENATAL APPOINTMENT: ⊏ YES ⊐   /   ⊏ NO ⊐

—— HIGHLIGHTS ——

ENERGY

1   5
O——————O——————O——————O——————O

MOOD

O——————O——————O——————O——————O

SLEEP

O——————O——————O——————O——————O

| BABY SIZE: *jicama* | |

CRAVINGS:

• _____
• _____
• _____
• _____

AVERSIONS:

• _____
• _____
• _____
• _____

8 WEEKS *to go*

—— THINGS I WANT TO REMEMBER: ——

YOU ARE MY SUNSHINE.

TODAY'S DATE: _____

PRENATAL APPOINTMENT: ⊏YES⊐   /   ⊏NO⊐

HIGHLIGHTS

ENERGY

1   5
O——O——O——O——O

MOOD

O——O——O——O——O

SLEEP

O——O——O——O——O

BABY SIZE: *pineapple*

CRAVINGS:

- _____
- _____
- _____
- _____

AVERSIONS:

- _____
- _____
- _____
- _____

7 **WEEKS** *to go*

THINGS I WANT TO REMEMBER:

TODAY'S DATE: _____

PRENATAL APPOINTMENT:　　⊏ YES ⊐　　/　　⊏ NO ⊐

HIGHLIGHTS

ENERGY

1 ○──○──○──○──○ 5

MOOD

○──○──○──○──○

SLEEP

○──○──○──○──○

BABY SIZE: *butternut squash*	

CRAVINGS:

- _____
- _____
- _____
- _____

AVERSIONS:

- _____
- _____
- _____
- _____

6 WEEKS *to go*

THINGS I WANT TO REMEMBER:

TODAY'S DATE: _____

PRENATAL APPOINTMENT: ⌐YES⌐ / ⌐NO⌐

┌─── HIGHLIGHTS ───┐

ENERGY

1   O—O—O—O—O   5

MOOD

O—O—O—O—O

SLEEP

O—O—O—O—O

BABY SIZE:
honeydew melon

CRAVINGS:

- _____
- _____
- _____
- _____

AVERSIONS:

- _____
- _____
- _____
- _____

5 WEEKS *to go*

┌─── THINGS I WANT TO REMEMBER: ───┐

TODAY'S DATE: _____

PRENATAL APPOINTMENT:　　⊏YES⊐　　/　　⊏NO⊐

HIGHLIGHTS

ENERGY

1　〇———〇———〇———〇———〇　5

MOOD

〇———〇———〇———〇———〇

SLEEP

〇———〇———〇———〇———〇

BABY SIZE: *romain lettuce*	

CRAVINGS:

- _____
- _____
- _____
- _____

AVERSIONS:

- _____
- _____
- _____
- _____

4 **WEEKS** *to go*

THINGS I WANT TO REMEMBER:

TODAY'S DATE: _____

PRENATAL APPOINTMENT: ⊏ YES ⊐ / ⊏ NO ⊐

HIGHLIGHTS

ENERGY
1 ——O———O———O———O———O 5

MOOD
O———O———O———O———O

SLEEP
O———O———O———O———O

| BABY SIZE: *swiss chard* | |

CRAVINGS:

- _____
- _____
- _____
- _____

AVERSIONS:

- _____
- _____
- _____
- _____

3 **WEEKS** *to go*

THINGS I WANT TO REMEMBER:

· trimester 3 ·

TODAY'S DATE: _____

PRENATAL APPOINTMENT: ⌐ YES ⌐   /   ⌐ NO ⌐

┌─────── HIGHLIGHTS ───────┐
│   │
│   │
│   │
│   │
│   │
│   │
│   │
│   │
│   │
│   │
└──────────────────────────┘

ENERGY

1   5
○────○────○────○────○

MOOD

○────○────○────○────○

SLEEP

○────○────○────○────○

BABY SIZE:
pumpkin

CRAVINGS:

- _____
- _____
- _____
- _____

AVERSIONS:

- _____
- _____
- _____
- _____

2 WEEKS *to go*

┌─────── THINGS I WANT TO REMEMBER: ───────┐
│   │
│   │
│   │
│   │
│   │
│   │
│   │
│   │
│   │
│   │
│   │
└──┘

· trimester 3 ·

TODAY'S DATE: _____

PRENATAL APPOINTMENT:　　⊏ YES ⊐　　/　　⊏ NO ⊐

┌─────── HIGHLIGHTS ───────┐

ENERGY
1　○──────○──────○──────○──────○　5

MOOD
○──────○──────○──────○──────○

SLEEP
○──────○──────○──────○──────○

BABY SIZE:
watermelon

CRAVINGS:
- _____
- _____
- _____
- _____

AVERSIONS:
- _____
- _____
- _____
- _____

1 **WEEKS** *to go*

┌─────── THINGS I WANT TO REMEMBER: ───────┐

TODAY'S DATE: _____

PRENATAL APPOINTMENT: ⌐YES⌐ / ⌐NO⌐

┌─── HIGHLIGHTS ───┐

ENERGY

1 ○──○──○──○──○ 5

MOOD

○──○──○──○──○

SLEEP

○──○──○──○──○

BABY SIZE: *jack fruit*

CRAVINGS:

- _____
- _____
- _____
- _____

AVERSIONS:

- _____
- _____
- _____
- _____

0 WEEKS *to go*

┌─── THINGS I WANT TO REMEMBER: ───┐

· trimester 3 ·

71

Third trimester reflections....

place
photo
here

photo details:_____

_____

_____

YOU ARE MY GREATEST ADVENTURE.

YOU'LL NEVER KNOW DEAR...

HOW MUCH I LOVE YOU.

YOU ARE SO LOVED.